FROM PHARAOH TO FREEDOM

The Story of the Passover in the
Old and New Testaments

**A Musical by
ROGER JONES**

For choir, soloists, piano and narrator
with optional drama and instrumental parts

NATIONAL CHRISTIAN EDUCATION COUNCIL
Robert Denholm House
Nutfield, Redhill, Surrey, RH1 4HW

TO SALLY PHILIPPA

COMPOSER'S NOTE

The story of Passover is a unique visual aid to the Gospel and FROM PHARAOH TO FREEDOM is intended to demonstrate the vital relationship between the Jewish Festival and the Christian Celebration of Holy Communion.

The Musical may be produced in two ways:
  Concert Version: Cantata, oratorio style, with Choir, Soloists and Narrator
  Drama Version: Actors/Soloists, Chorus, with costumes, dance, etc.
In either version audience participation is desirable, enhancing the Work as an act of worship. The accompaniment may be either on 'live' instruments or on tape.

I would like to extend my thanks to a number of people for their help in the preparation of this Musical. First, to my wife for the way she has tolerated the family disruption which always seems to accompany the writing of a Work; then to the members of the East Birmingham Renewal Group for their counsel and support; to Victoria Richmond for suggestions about the drama; also to Dave Anfield, my recording producer, for helpful comments and suggestions.

FROM PHARAOH TO FREEDOM has a message for all. In our experience the greatest impact will be made when the rehearsals include Bible teaching and prayer times. My prayer is that this Musical will bring many into a realisation of the liberty and power that Jesus Christ gives— indeed FROM PHARAOH TO FREEDOM.

Birmingham   Roger Jones

FROM PHARAOH TO FREEDOM—items available

Score, Words edition, Audience leaflet
Published by National Christian Education Council

Record, Cassette, Accompaniment tape
Released by Anfield Music Ltd

Orchestral parts, Production notes, Choir Bible study outlines
Published by Christian Music Ministries
(apply in first instance through NCEC enclosing two postage stamps)

Other Works by Roger Jones published by NCEC
Greater than Gold—the story of Mary Jones and her Bible
Saints Alive!—on the beginning of the Church
A Grain of Mustard Seed—on the life of Robert Raikes

Works by Roger Jones by other publishers
Jerusalem Joy, Stargazers, David, Apostle

Cover logo designed by Tim Seaward, © Anfield Music Ltd

ISBN 0–7917–0444–8
Music setting by P. T. Vinson, Norwich, Norfolk
Typesetting by Avonset, Midsomer Norton, Bath
Printed and bound by The Whitefriars Press Ltd, Tonbridge, Kent

CONTENTS

CAST

Singers: (Bass)   Moses and Jesus
        (Tenor)   Aaron, brother of Moses
        (Alto)   Miriam, sister of Moses
        (Soprano) Elisheba, wife of Aaron

Eleazar ⎫
Rachel   ⎬ children of Aaron
Choir   ⎭ and Elisheba

Non-singers: Narrator
               Pharaoh

Dancers, various as: Soldiers
                       Slave-drivers
                       Plagues
                       Angel of Death

ACKNOWLEDGEMENTS

Scripture quotations marked (NIV) are from the Holy Bible, New International Version. Copyright © 1973, 1978, International Bible Society, published by Hodder & Stoughton.

Scripture quotations marked (GNB) are from the Good News Bible (The Bible Societies/Collins Publishers); Old Testament © American Bible Society 1976; New Testament © American Bible Society 1976.

FROM PHARAOH TO FREEDOM

Roger Jones (Op. 13)

1. PASSOVER

(Moses, Aaron, Miriam, Elisheba, Choir)

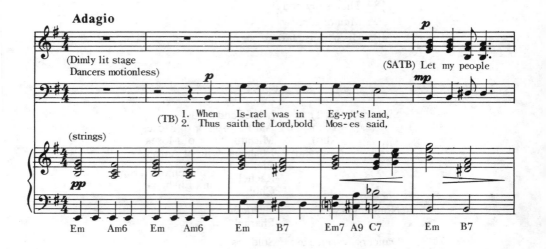

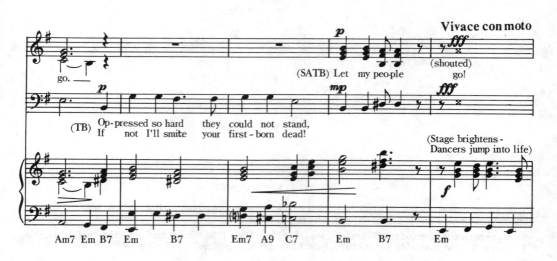

For this night of lib- er - ty!   (SATB) Wel - come to   the

B7   Em

cel - e - brat-ion!   This the night of lib - e - rat-ion!   Hear the news of   our sal - va-tion!

Am   D7   G   Am   B7   Em

(SA) From Phar-aoh we are free!   We cel - e-brate, our Pass-o-ver is here!
(SATB)

(TB) Dance and sing! ____

B7

7

This the night of lib - e - rat - ion! Hear the news of our sal - vat - ion!

D7   G   Am7   B7   Em

(SA) From Phar-aoh we are free! We cel - e - brate, our Pass-o-ver is

(SATB)

(TB) Dance and sing! _____

B7

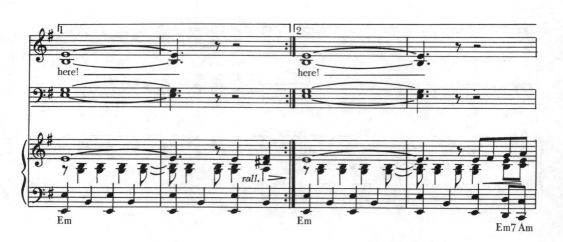

here! _____   here! _____

rall.

Em   Em   Em7 Am

Between Songs 1 and 2

NARRATOR: A new king came to power in Egypt. He said to his people, 'These Israelites are so numerous and strong that they are a threat to us. In case of war they might join our enemies in order to fight against us, and might escape from the country. We must find some way to keep them from becoming even more numerous.' So the Egyptians put slave-drivers over them to crush their spirits with hard labour. But the more the Egyptians oppressed the Israelites, the more they increased in number and the further they spread through the land. The Egyptians came to fear the Israelites and made their lives miserable by forcing them into cruel slavery. They made them work on their building projects and in their fields, and they had no mercy on them.

(Parts of Exodus 1.8–14, GNB)

2. HOSANNA

('Hosanna' is the cry of the slave: 'Save us, we beseech you.')
(Aaron, Miriam, Elisheba, Choir)

(Exit Moses. Dancers enter as Egyptian soldiers. They drag soloists from Table, turning them into Israelite slaves. Slave-driving mime throughout Song.)

(SATB) Ho - san – na! Ho - san – na! Have mer - cy on

A6   E   A6   E   A6

me.— Ho-san – na! Ho - san – na! Lord, set your

E   A6   E   A6   E

peo – ple free.— (SA) Ho-san – na! _____ Ho-

(TB) O Lord, save your peo-ple,

A6   E   A6   E   A   E   A

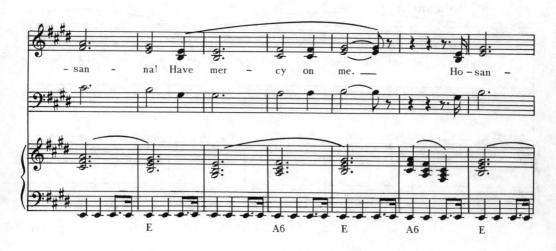

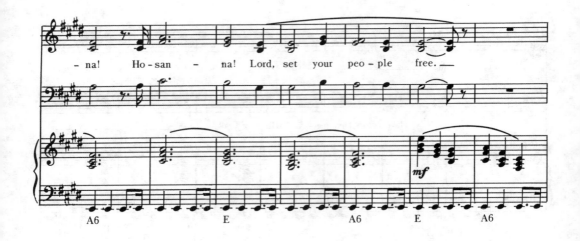

-na! Ho - san - na! Lord, set your peo - ple free. —

A6   E   A6   E   A6

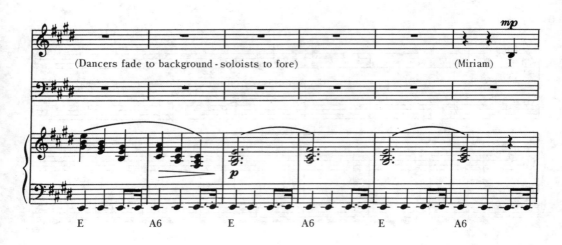

(Dancers fade to background - soloists to fore)   (Miriam) I

E   A6   E   A6   E   A6

C **Animato**

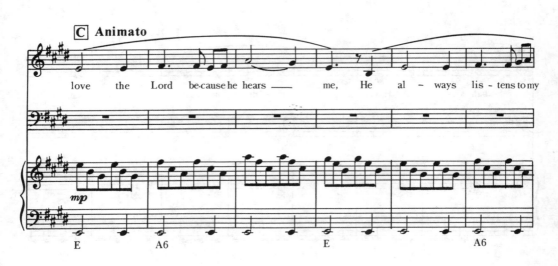

love the Lord be-cause he hears — me, He al - ways lis - tens to my

E   A6   E   A6

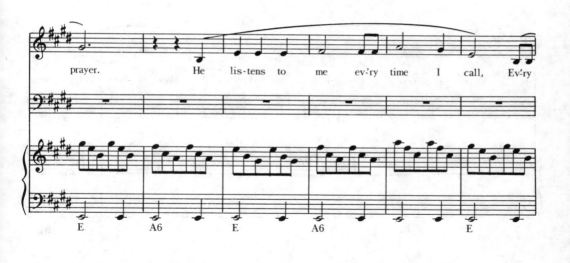

prayer. He lis-tens to me ev'ry time I call, Ev'ry

E   A6   E   A6   E

time I call on him. (Elisheba Miriam) The dan – ger of death was

A6   E   A6   E

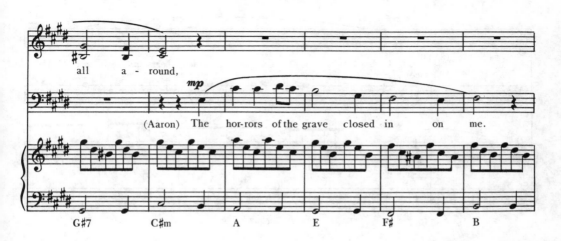

all a - round,

mp

(Aaron) The hor-rors of the grave closed in on me.

G#7   C#m   A   E   F#   B

(Elisheba
Miriam
Aaron) Filled with fear I called to the Lord, (Elisheba) I beg you, Lord, (Trio) Save

A   E   G#7   C#m   A   A6   B7

me.

E   A6   E   A6   F   Gm7

(SATB
+
Audience) I love the Lord be-cause he hears —— me, He

F   Gm7   F   Gm7   Gm7   F

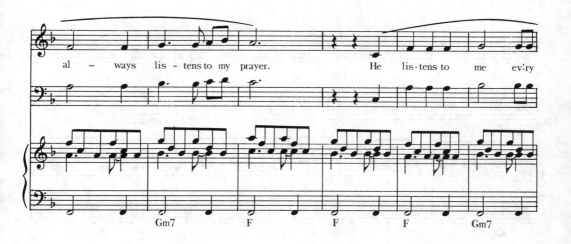

al — ways lis - tens to my prayer. He lis - tens to me ev'ry

Gm7   F   F   F   Gm7

time I call, Ev'ry time I call on him. (SA) The

F   Gm   F

dan - ger of death was all a - round,

(TB) The hor - rors of the grave closed

Gm7   F   A7   Dm   Bb   F

Filled with fear, I called to the Lord,

in on me.

G7　　C7　　Bb　　F　　A7　　Dm

beg you, Lord, ___

(A) I beg you, Lord, ___ (All) Save me.

(TB) I beg you, Lord, ___

Bb　　Gm7　　Bb　　Gm7　 C7　F　　Gm7

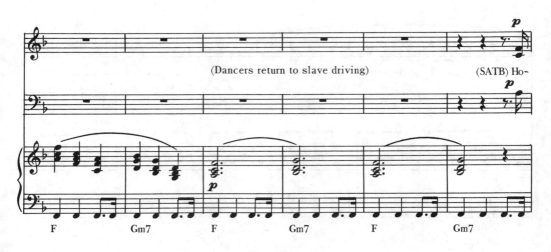

(Dancers return to slave driving) (SATB) Ho~

F　　Gm7　　F　　Gm7　　F　　Gm7

16

17

19

Between Songs 2 and 3
NARRATOR: One day while Moses was taking care of the sheep and goats of his father-in-law Jethro, he led the flock across the desert and came to Sinai, the holy mountain. There the angel of the Lord appeared to him as a flame coming from the middle of a bush.

(Parts of Exodus 3.1–2, GNB)

3. FACE TO FACE?
(Moses, Aaron, Choir)

still it stays the same? / com-ing from the flame!

Dm7

I must move clos-er to see, / Call-ing to me by my name!

B♭M7   Gm9   Asus4

I must move clos-er to see! / Call-ing to me by my name!

B♭M7   Gm9   Asus4   A

A Maestoso

mf

(SATB + Aud.) Face to face with God? _____ Face to face with the

D   G   Asus4   A   D   G

Lord? _____ How can this be? How come this

Asus4   A   F   G   D   F   G

21

mys·ter·y?___ That he should come close to me! _____ The living.

D   F   G   F   G   Asus4   A

B **Allegro con aggressione**

___ God! _____

NARRATOR (v.4) The Lord said,

D   G   D   G   Dm

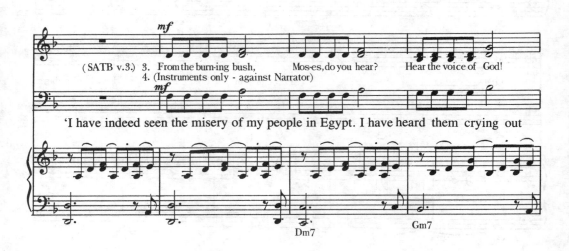

(SATB v.3.) 3. From the burn-ing bush,   Mos-es, do you hear?   Hear the voice of God!
4. (Instruments only - against Narrator)

'I have indeed seen the misery of my people in Egypt. I have heard them crying out

Dm7   Gm7

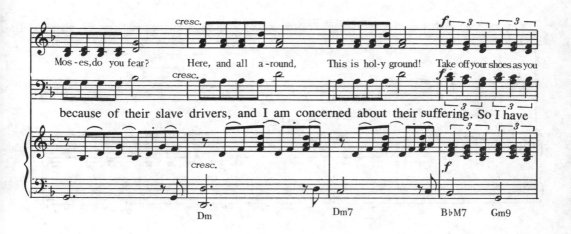

cresc.

Mos-es, do you fear? Here, and all a-round, This is hol-y ground! Take off your shoes as you

because of their slave drivers, and I am concerned about their suffering. So I have

f

Dm   Dm7   BbM7   Gm9

pray.   Take off your shoes as you pray! _____

come down to rescue them and to bring them into a good and spacious land, a land

Asus4   BbM7   Gm9   Asus4

A

C

mf

(SATB Face   to   face   with   God? _____   Face   to
+ Aud.   *mf* (v.4 Instruments only)
v.3)

flowing with milk and honey. So now, go. I am sending you to Pharaoh to bring my

mf

D   G   Asus4   A   D

23

face with the Lord? _____ (v.4.Choir) *Ah* How can this be?

people the Israelites out of Egypt.'

Ah How come this mys-ter-y? _____ *Ah* That he should come close to me! _____

The liv-ing God! _____

During Song 3 (after verse 4)
NARRATOR: *But Moses began to make excuses, saying,*
  'I am nobody. How can I go to the king? When I go to the Israelites, what can I tell them?
Suppose the Israelites do not believe me and will not listen to what I say. What shall I do?'
Each time the Lord answered Moses with miracles and promises of his power.
  But Moses said, 'No, Lord, don't send me. I am a poor speaker. Lord, please send someone
else.'
  At this the Lord became angry with Moses and said, 'What about your brother Aaron? I
know that he can speak well. He is now coming to meet you. You can speak to him and tell
him what to say. I will help both of you to speak, and I will tell you both what to do.'
  (Parts of Exodus 3.11,13; 4.1,10,13–15, GNB)

3. Reprise

27

God! ——— The liv-ing —— God! ————

D   G   D

(Exit Moses & Aaron)

Between Songs 3 and 4
NARRATOR: Moses and Aaron brought together all the elders of the Israelites, and Aaron
told them everything the Lord had said to Moses. He also performed the signs before the
people, and they believed. And when they heard that the Lord was concerned about them and
had seen their misery, they bowed down and worshipped. Afterwards Moses and Aaron went
to Pharaoh.

(Parts of Exodus 4.29 to 5.1, NIV)

4. LET'S GO, PHARAOH!
(Moses, Aaron, Miriam, Rachel, Eleazar, Choir)

(TB) Go down,   Mos-es,   way   down   in   E-gypt's land,

Em Am6   Em   Am6   Em   B7   Em7   A9   CM7   Em

Nile — is turned — in-to blood!
ev — en get in — to your bed!
kill ev'-ry cam — el and mule!

Ah

You won't feel well, — you'll get
Then there'll be gnats,—They'll start
Cat — tle and sheep, — they will

B7   Em   Am

sick of the smell,—And to drink it will do — you no good. (Eleazor: Agh!)
driv-ing you bats!—And you'll wake up next morn-ing with dread (Cast to improvise swotting Gnats!)
die as you sleep,—And if still you re-fuse you're a fool. (Rachel "Did you hear that?
Pharaoh,a fool!")

Em   F   B7   (Guitar Tacet)

C

(Choir finger flicks resume)

(Aaron) Let my peo-ple go! Y'got-ta

Em B7   Em B7   Em B7   Em B7   Em B7   Em B7

do what the Lord has said! — (Moses) Let my peo-ple go! Y'd bet-ta do it or y'll end up dead!

Em D C Bm Em B7 Em B7 Em D

D

(Aaron) "Pharaoh, will you let us go this time?" (Pharaoh) "No!"

— (Moses + Aaron) Do it or y'll end up dead! —

C Bm Em D C Bm Em B7 Em B7 Em B7

(Miriam) 4. Let's go, Pharaoh! Just see what you have caused! —
(Choir finger flicks end)

Em B7 Em B7 Em B7 Em B7 Em B7

33

Dark-ness! Dark-ness! Dark-ness ov - er you.

F   F♯   F   F♯   Gdim

F

(Choir finger flicks resume - until Coda)

(Lights up)

(Rachel /Eleazor Miriam)   Let   my   peo ple go!

(Aaron)

(Moses Aaron)   Let   my   peo ple go! Y' gotta

Fm   C7   Fm   C7   Fm   C7   Fm   C7   Fm   C7   Fm   C7

Let   my   peo ple go!   (Aaron)

do what the Lord has said!_   Let   my   peo ple go! Y'd bet-ta do it or y'll end up   dead!_

Fm   E♭   D♭   Cm   Fm   C7   Fm   C7   Fm   E♭

34

Go!

(Aaron) Do it or y'll end up dead!

(Instrumental verse - dancing around Pharoah)

35

36

peo-ple go! — Let my peo-ple go! Yes? Yes? Yes? No!
(All) _____ (Pharaoh)

Fm   C7   Fm   Eb7   Bb7 Bbm6

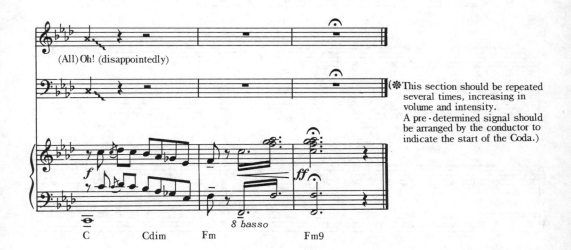

(All) Oh! (disappointedly)

(❋This section should be repeated several times, increasing in volume and intensity.
A pre-determined signal should be arranged by the conductor to indicate the start of the Coda.)

C   Cdim   Fm   8 basso   Fm9

Between Songs 4 and 5

NARRATOR: Moses said, 'This is what the Lord says: "About midnight I will go throughout Egypt. Every first born son in Egypt will die. There will be loud wailing throughout Egypt." All these officials of yours will come to me, bowing down before me and saying, "Go, you and all the people who follow you!" After that I will leave.' Then Moses, hot with anger, left Pharaoh.

  Then Moses summoned all the elders of Israel and said to them, 'Go at once and select the animals for your families and slaughter the Passover lamb. Take a bunch of hyssop, dip it into the blood in the basin and put some of the blood on the top and on both sides of the door-frame. Not one of you shall go out of the door of his house until morning. When the Lord goes through the land, he will see the blood on the top and sides of the door-frame and will pass over that doorway.'

(Parts of Exodus 11.4–6,8; 12.21–23, NIV)

5. WHEN I SEE THE BLOOD
(Choir, Miriam, Elisheba, Aaron)

Andante cantabile

Soloists, to Table - during this song
the Meal is eaten, but first the blood (SATB)
is applied to the door - frame. or Solo

When I see the blood I will pass ov - er you, For
then I'll know that you be - long to me. _____ When I see the blood I will pass
ov - er you. My peo - ple, don't you see, I want you to be free! I'll

see the blood! I will pass ov-er you. When I see the blood I will pass ov-er you, For

Em7   A7   D   D   G   A   D

then I'll know that you be-long to me. _____ When I see the blood I will pass

D   G   A7sus4 A   D   G

ov-er you. My peo-ple, don't you see, I want you to be free! I'll

A   D   Em7   A   F♯m7   Bm

39

NARRATOR: At midnight the Lord struck down all the first born in Egypt, from the first born of Pharaoh, who sat on the throne, to the first born of the prisoner, who was in the dungeon. There was loud wailing in Egypt, for there was not a house without someone dead. *But the angel of death passed over the houses of the Israelites.*

(Parts of Exodus 12.29–30, NIV)

41

42

44

45

D   Em7   A   D   (Exit all)

Between Songs 5 and 6
NARRATOR: During the night Pharaoh summoned Moses and Aaron and said, 'Up! Leave
my people, you and the Israelites! Go. Take your flocks and herds, and go.' The Egyptians
urged the people to hurry and leave the country. 'For otherwise,' they said, 'we will all die!'
(Parts of Exodus 12.31–33, NIV)

6. LET'S ALL GO!
(Moses, Elisheba, Aaron, Miriam, Choir)

Allegretto con brio

(Enter Elisheba, Miriam & Dancers)   (Choir/Dancers Finger flicks)

Em   B7   Em   B7   Em   B7   Em   B7

Choir shouts

Go!   Go!   Go!

Em   B7   Em   B7   Em   B7   Em   B7   Em   B7

47

48

50

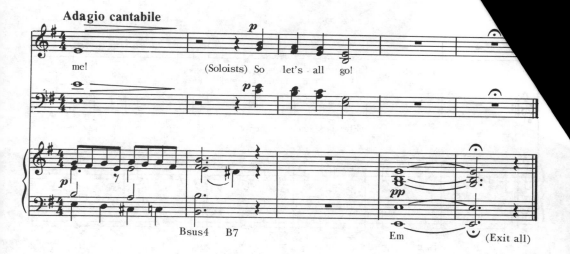

Adagio cantabile

me!

(Soloists) So let's all go!

Bsus4   B7

Em   (Exit all)

Between Songs 6 and 7
NARRATOR: The Israelites set out on foot. There were about six hundred thousand men, not
counting women and children. A large number of other people and many sheep, goats, and
cattle also went with them.
   On that day the Lord brought the Israelite tribes out of Egypt.
   During the day the Lord went in front of them in a pillar of cloud to show them the way, and
during the night he went in front of them in a pillar of fire to give them light, so that they could
travel night and day.

(Parts of Exodus 12.37–38,51; 13.21, GNB)

7. GUIDE ME, O MY GREAT REDEEMER
(Elisheba, Children, Choir)

Tune: Ward End

Words by William Williams and others

Andante con moto
(Elisheba)

(Enter Elisheba, Rachel & Eleazor)

C   Em   Dm7   G7   C   Em   Dm7   G   C   Em   Dm7   G7

(...heba) 1. Guide me, O my great Re-deem-er,
2. O - pen now the cry-stal foun-tain,

(Eleazor & Rachel - v.2 only) 2. O — pen now the cry-stal

C   Em   Dm7   G7   C   Em   F   G7   C   Em   Dm7   G7

Pil – grim through this bar – ren land;   I   am
Where   the heal – ing wat – ers flow: Let   the

foun-tain,   Where   the   heal – ing   wat-ers   flow:

C   Em   F   G7   C   Em   Dm7   G7   C   Em

weak, but you are might – y,   Hold   me   with your power - ful
fire and cloud – y   pil – lar   Lead   me   all   my   jour – ney

Let   the   fire   and cloud – y   pil-lar

Fm   G7   C   Em   Dm7   G7   C   Em   F   G7

Ev - er   be my strength and shield.

F   G7   C   Em   Dm7   G7   C   Em   Dm7   G7

B

(Elisheba
Rachel &
Eleazor)

3. When   I   tread the verge of   Jor-dan,

(Choir +Audience)   When   I   tread the verge of

cresc.   mf

Db   Fm   Ebm7   Ab7   Db   Fm   Gb   Ab7   Db   Fm   Ebm7   Ab7

Bid   my anxious fears sub-side;   Death   of   death, and hell's des -

Jor-dan,   Bid   my   anx-ious fears sub-side;

Db   Fm   Gb   Ab7   Db   Fm   Ebm7   Ab7   Db   Fm   Gb   Ab7

ev-er sing to you. | I will ev-er sing to

I will ev-er sing to you.

Gb   Db   Fm   Ebm7 Ab7   Db   Fm   Gb   Ab7

rall. *pp*

you. This section to be repeated several times - eventually accompaniment stops - I will ev-er sing! ___

I will ev-er sing to you. I will ev-er sing! ___

Db   Fm   Gb   Ab7

(Enter rest of Soloists)

Between Songs 7 and 8
NARRATOR: Moses said to the people, 'Remember this day — the day on which you left Egypt, the place where you were slaves. This is the day the Lord brought you out by his great power.'

(Part of Exodus 13.3, GNB)

The Jews were told to celebrate it for all time to come. And they have done this ever since, whether in exile, under oppression, or at home in the promised land. Just as on one unforgettable night in Jerusalem nearly two thousand years ago, when Jesus and his friends gathered in an upper room to eat their Passover meal.

8. THIS IS MY BODY
(Jesus and disciples [Miriam, Rachel, Eleazar], Choir)

Andante con moto

D   A   Bm   F#m   G

58

blood,   Poured out for   you.

D   Em7   A7   D   A   D

B *mf*

(SATB +
Aud.)   Take,   eat,   this is his bod-y,—

(During the Choruses the Bread & Wine are passed around the cast)

A   D   A   Bm   F#m

This is his bod-y,—   brok-en for   you! ——— Take,

G   D   Em7   A   D

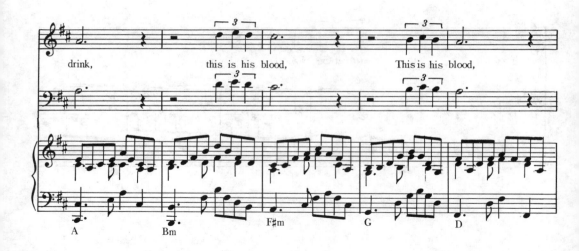

drink, this is his blood, This is his blood,

A   Bm   F#m   G   D

3rd time to ⊕

poured out for you!

3rd time to ⊕

Em7   A7   D   A   D   A

C (v.1 Miriam
v.2 Rachel/Eleazor)

mp

1. Be - hold ⎯ the Lamb, ⎯
2. This, this ⎯ is love, ⎯

Be-hold the Lamb of
But not that we loved

D   A   Bm   D   G   D

this is my blood, This is my blood, poured out for

Bm F#m G D Em7 A7

più mosso

you. _____

(1st time - All Soloists
2nd time - SATB
+ Audience)

Face to

D G D G D

face with God! _____ Face to face with my Lord! _____

G Asus4 A D G Asus4

Between Songs 8 and 9
NARRATOR: *What was it the prophet Isaiah wrote?*
   'We despised him and rejected him;
      he endured suffering and pain.
   But he endured the suffering that should have been ours,
      the pain that we should have borne.
   All of us were like sheep that were lost,
      each of us going his own way.
   But the Lord made the punishment fall on him,
      the punishment all of us deserved.
   Like a lamb about to be slaughtered,
   like a sheep about to be sheared,
      he never said a word.
   He took the place of many sinners
      and prayed that they might be forgiven.'

(Isaiah 53.3a,4a,6,7b,12c, GNB)

9. MAN OF SORROWS
(Elisheba, Choir)

Tune: Burney Lane

Words by Philipp Bliss

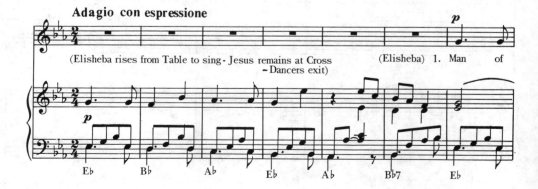

sor-rows! What a name ____ For the Son of God, who came ____

Bb   Ab   Eb   Ab   Eb   Fm7

cresc.   _mf_
Ruin - ed sin-ners to re - claim! ____ Hal- le - lu – jah! What a

Bb   Eb   Cm   Ab   F7   Eb   Cm

A

Sav - iour! ____

Fm7   Bb7   Eb   Bb   Ab   Eb   Ab

_mp_
(Elisheba) 2. Bear – ing shame and scoff-ing rude, ____ In my

(SA) Bear – ing shame and scoff – ing

Bb7   Eb   Bb   Ab   Eb   Ab

place con-demned he stood; ____ Sealed my par-don with his blood: ____

rude, In my place con-demned he stood; Sealed my

mf

cresc.

Eb   Fm7   Bb7   Eb   Cm   Ab

B

___ Hal – le – lu – jah! What a Sav – iour! ___

par-don with his blood: Hal – le – lu – jah! What a Sav – iour!

F7   Eb   Cm   Fm7   Bb7   Eb

mp

p

(SATB) 3. Guilt – y, vile, and help-less

p

Bb   Ab   Eb   Ab   Bb7   Eb   Bb

66

C (Instrumental Verse) (Enter Solo Dancer [Angel of Death] - moves around Cross)

67

(Exit Dancer) **D** *p*

(Elisheba) 4. Lift - ed up was he to die; ——— 'It is fin-ished!' was his

(S) Ah ——————— ah ———————

Bb7 Eb Bb Ab Eb Ab Eb

cry; ——— Now in heav'n ex-alt - ed high: ——— Hal- le - lu - jah!

Ah ——————

Fm7 Bb7 Eb Cm Ab F7 Eb

E *rall.*

What a Sav - iour! ——

(Jesus comes from Cross to embrace rest of Soloists)

rall.

Cm Fm7 Bb7 Eb Bb Ab Eb B7

68

(Elisheba SATB + Audience) 5. When he comes, our glorious King, All his ransomed home to bring, Then anew this song we'll sing:

(Choir) Hal-le-lu-jah!

(Elisheba) Hal-le-lu-jah!

(All) Hal - le - lu - jah! What a Sav - iour!

(Soloists to Table)

Between Songs 9 and 10
NARRATOR: *The Apostle Peter, who was with Jesus at the Passover meal, wrote:*
But you are the chosen race, the King's priests, the holy nation, God's own people, chosen to proclaim the wonderful acts of God, who called you out of darkness into his own marvellous light.

(*1 Peter 2.9, GNB*)

(*A short talk suitable for the occasion may be given at this point.*)

For, as St Paul declared,
Christ, our Passover lamb, has been sacrificed for us. So let us celebrate!

(*The whole choir should join in this final shout: CELEBRATE!*)

10. HIS LOVE IS ETERNAL

(Based on Psalm 118)
(All Soloists, Choir)

Is-ra-el say:＿ (All) His love＿is e - ter - nal! All who wor-ship him may now say:
(Eleazor)

(All) His love＿ is e - ter - nal!

(SATB +Audience) O give thanks to the Lord!＿ His love＿is e - ter - nal!

O give thanks to the Lord!_ His love_ is e- ter- nal! O in my dis-tress I called
(Rachel)

D   A7   D   G   D   A7   D   G   A7

out to the Lord!_ (All) His love_ is e - ter - nal! He re-plied by set-ting me free!
(Rachel)

D   G   D   E9   A7   G   A7   D

B

(All) His love_ is e- ter- nal!

G   D   A7   Eb   Bb7   Eb   Bb7   Eb   Bb7

73

(SATB + Audience) O give thanks to the Lord! His love is e - ter - nal!

O give thanks to the Lord! His love is e - ter - nal! The stone which the build-ers re-
(Rachel & Eleazor)

- jec-ted, dis-owned, His love is e - ter - nal! Has be-come the chief corner-stone!
(All) (Rachel & Eleazor)

74

thanks to the Lord!_ His love_ is e - ter - nal!

D Vivace con moto

(Enter Dancers)

Eb   Ab   Eb   Bb7   Eb   Em

mf
Ah _____   Ah _____

(SATB)
mf

Am   D7   G   Am   B7   Em   B7

Ah _____

E *mf*

(Elisheba Moses)   This is a time for

mf

B7   Em

76

song, (Elisheba Miriam) This is a time for danc-ing. (Elisheba Miriam Aaron Moses) *mf* O we have wait-ed long

For this night of lib-er - ty! (SATB) Wel-come to the

cel-e - bra-tion! This the night of lib - e - rat-ion! Hear the news of our sal-va-tion!

B7   Em   E   Am

B7   Em

Am   D7   G   Am   B7   Em

(SA) From Phar–aoh we are free! We cel – e – brate, our Pass – o – ver is

(SATB)

(TB) Dance and sing! ——————

B7

F *mf*

here! (SATB) Lai, lai, lai, lai, lai, lai

mf

Em B7

(SA) Lai, lai, lai, lai, lai, lai, lai (SATB) Lai, lai, lai, lai, lai, lai, lai

Em E Am

78

Lai, lai, lai, lai, lai, lai, lai

B7

Em

Wel-come to the cel - e - bra-tion! This the night of lib - e - rat-ion!

Am

D7

G

Hear the news of our sal - vat-ion! (SA) From

(TB) Dance and sing!

Am7

B7

Em

B7